For Conor and Sadhbh
ED and JG

For Gary, Emma, Katie, Mum and Dad
SG

*This is
my photo*

My name is

....

The Story of Patrick

First published in 2008

Childnames.net
27 Villarea Park, Glenageary, Co. Dublin, Ireland
info@childnames.net
www.childnames.net
Tel +353 87 936 9888

Written by Eithne Diamond and John Gallagher

Illustrations by Sandra Gibson
Additional illustrative input by DVD

Further illustrative input,
layout and pre-press: Ferret on the Dartboard

Text and illustrations copyright Eithne Diamond and John Gallagher

ISBN 978-1-906326-09-8

Design concept: DVD; Layout: Ferret on the Dartboard
Printed in China by Ming Tai Printing Co Ltd

The Story of Patrick

Eithne Diamond and John Gallagher

Illustrations: Sandra Gibson

Childnames.net

Patrick :

the facts for big people

- The name Patrick comes from the Latin *patricius*, meaning 'nobleman.'

  - Tradition says he was born into a wealthy family on the west coast of Britain.

    - His father, Calpurnius, was a church deacon and politician. His grandfather, Potitus, was a priest.

    - When Patrick was 16 his town was attacked by Irish raiders, led by Niall of the Nine Hostages according to some versions.

- He was taken prisoner and sold to a chieftain named Milchiú to herd animals on Slemish mountain, near Ballymena, County Antrim.

- After six years in slavery legend says that a voice told him to "go to the coast, there is a ship to take you home".

- He returned to his family but dreamt of voices calling him back to Ireland.

- He became a priest in France, perhaps at Lerins Abbey on an island in the French Riveria.

- Later he became a bishop and in 432 was sent to Ireland by Pope Paladius.

- Patrick's first church in Ireland was in Saul, County Down.

- He is said to have created the country's first holy wells close to Downpatrick, County Down.

- When he died, the Book of Armagh says his body was carried by oxen to a hill in Downpatrick, where Down Cathedral was later built.

- St Patrick's Centre in the town now attracts 120,000 visitors a year.

- According to tradition Patrick built a stone church in Armagh city around 445 AD. Today Armagh holds the primary cathedrals of the Catholic and Protestant churches, both named after the saint.

- Croagh Patrick is a mountain in Co Mayo, where Patrick reputedly spent 40 days fasting. Legend says he was attacked by demon birds and the devil's mother, after which he banished all snakes from Ireland.

- As there may never have been snakes in Ireland, the story is symbolic of Patrick converting people to Christianity and banishing the pagan Druids, whose symbol was a serpent.

- In ancient times the mountain was used to celebrate the pagan feast of Lug at the start of harvest time.

- Today it attracts 40,000 pilgrims annually on the last day of July, for a 765 m (2,500 ft) trek to its summit.

- St Patrick's Purgatory, on Lough Derg, Co Donegal, is a second place of pilgrimage and fasting. Legend says Patrick had a vision of the after-life in a cave there.

- A related legend says that when Patrick banished the serpents, the snake of pride escaped to Lough Derg. It could only be cast out by prayer and fasting, hence the basis for the pilgrimage.

- Another Patrick legend tells of the High King of Laoghaire holding a pagan feast during which he lit a fire on the Hill of Tara, Co Meath. Patrick outraged the king by lighting a Christian fire nearby, at Slane, which was inextinguishable. The King's druids and Patrick changed the climate and elements at their will, in a battle of miracles which Patrick finally won.

- Other tales record arguments between Patrick and the legendary Oisín on his return from Tír na nOg, on the struggle between pagan and Christian values and physical strength and mystical power.

- St Patrick explained the Christian mystery of the Holy Trinity with the three-leafed shamrock plant, now Ireland's national emblem.

- Patrick has left two major written works. The *Confessions* gives details of his early life, while *The Lorica* is a famous Christian prayer beginning "Christ on my right side, Christ on my left …".

- Internationally there is a St Patrick's town in Missouri, USA and Saint-Patrice-sur-Loire, in France.

- St Patrick's Chair in the Isle of Man, one of the oldest religious sites on the island, is where Patrick reputedly blessed the local population.

- March 17th is celebrated as St Patrick's Day and a national holiday not only in Ireland, but also on the Caribbean island of Montserrat. St Patrick's town on the island was largely destroyed by a volcanic eruption in 1997.

- The first recorded Patrick's Day parade was in America in 1737. St Patrick's Festival in Dublin is the main event of the Irish St Patrick's week celebrations around March 17th.

- St Patrick is also worshipped in the Orthodox church, with a number of Orthodox icons dedicated to him.

Patrick :

the story for little people

O nce there was a boy named Patrick. Patrick's home was near the sea. Every day, after school, he went to the beach to build sand castles.

Sometimes he watched the seabirds searching for fish. Other times he checked the sand for unusual seashells. Every day he looked out to sea at ships sailing past.

One day, while Patrick was playing on the beach, he heard a loud splash in a rock pool nearby. When he turned around he saw a large octopus looking up at him.

"Patrick! Patrick! Have you seen my phone? I must have dropped it when the tide washed me in," the octopus said crossly.

Patrick gasped. "How did you know my name? Oh, never mind, you can use my phone if you wish."

The octopus grabbed the phone with its eight arms and dived back into the water. Patrick was so amazed that he did not notice a large ship casting its shadow on the beach.

13

When Patrick looked around he saw
a pirate ship with a large black flag
on top. Pirates were running ashore.

The first pirate was playing a violin
and looked very happy. The
second was clutching a big book
called 'U2 by U2' and looked
very, very happy. The third pirate
was carrying a large sword and
looked very, very cross.

Even worse, he was running towards Patrick.

"Yo, ho, my laddie. You'll do nicely for
minding the sheep on my brother's farm!"
he shouted.

The pirates carried Patrick on to their ship and sailed back out to sea.

Suddenly Patrick realised he did not have a phone to contact home. "My mum always warned me not to give my phone to strangers. Now nobody will know where I am," he sighed.

Before long the ship arrived at land again. They were met by a strange old man, wearing one green shoe and one orange shoe.

"Hello, my name is Milchiú," he said.

He pointed to a mountain covered in mist. "Your job will be to mind my sheep and protect them from the horrid snakes," he said.

He grabbed Patrick by the arm and rushed off while the pirates shouted after them.

When Patrick reached the mountain
there were snakes everywhere.

"The snakes tease my sheep.
They steal their food during the day.
They make screechy noises at
bedtime," Milchiú said.

"Now they're starting to tease me
as well," he said, as a small snake
wearing sun glasses made
a funny face and
went 'Blahhhh.'

Every day after that Patrick chased snakes
over the mountain.

At first the snakes were scared
and hid under rocks.
Then they became annoyed
and shouted "Catch us if you
can! Catch us if you can!"

"That will teach you to stop
annoying us," they laughed.

Patrick got very fed up indeed.
But Milchiú still made him chase the snakes.

One night Patrick decided he had had enough.

He checked that Milchiú was asleep.
He checked that the snakes were asleep.
He checked that the sheep were asleep, especially
the one that always shouted "Milchiú, Patrick's not
working!" whenever he took a rest during the day.

Then Patrick ran away. He was so fit from
chasing snakes over the mountain that he
soon reached the sea. There he met the
pirates again.

"Please take me home," he cried.

The very, very cross pirate stared at him
for a second. "OK, we'll take you. That will teach
my brother to pay his bills in future," he said.

Before he knew it, Patrick was home again.
His mum was very happy to see him
and gave him a big hug. He told her
all about the pirates and sheep
and snakes.

He didn't think she believed him,
though, when he told her that
an octopus had stolen his phone.

Soon he was again playing by the seaside every day. However every night he dreamt of snakes chasing the sheep.

Even worse, the snakes were getting naughtier and naughtier, chasing people and birds and animals from their homes.

"It's not fair, I'm the only person those snakes are afraid of!" Patrick thought.

The next day Patrick went shopping.

"I want a large pointed hat, to stop
the snakes pulling my hair. I want a
large stick with a hook at the end,
to catch even the biggest snake
and fling him into the sea," he told
the shopkeeper.

"Oh, and I also need an iPod. I don't
think they sell CDs where I'm travelling
to," he added.

Then he hired a small boat. On a very
clear and sunny day, with a high, misty
mountain in the distance across
the waves, he set sail. He was going
to teach those snakes a lesson
they would never forget!

What's in a name?
– more facts for big people

- When actress Betty Joan Perske was given the screen name Lauren Bacall one of the most popular first names for girls of recent decades was created.

- *The name Keira did not exist until the 21st century, except as a misspelling!*

- It is soaring up the baby name charts due to the success of UK-born actress Keira Knightly. She changed the spelling from Kiera to avoid mispronunciation in Hollywood.

- *Today there are thousands of first names. Even the most popular names may account for only 2–3% of the overall total.*

- There were far fewer names in previous centuries. Baptism registers in the UK during the second half of the 16th century record that one in five boys was named William.

- *During the second half of the 18th century, just three names – Elizabeth, Mary and Anne – accounted for 57% of all girls born in the UK.*

- As recently as the early 20th century, some first names were so common in Ireland that a second 'first' name was added for identification, often based on a parent's first name: hence the character Paidín Mike in Synge's famous play 'The Playboy of the Western World.'

- *In the north of England, until the late 19th century, many people relied on multiple names to convey family identity – for instance, Tom o'Dick o'Mary's.*

- Today's parents increasingly use original and inventive first names as a means of conveying identity and 'brand' to their children.

- *Back in the 16th century, however, the Council of Trent ruled that Catholics could name their children only after canonised saints or angels.*

- During the same period, in Britain and USA the Puritans insisted that only names from the Bible were valid. They later allowed names such as Livewell and Safe-on-high.

- *Without any edicts, the double name John Paul suddenly became popular in Ireland after the Pope visited the country in 1979.*

- From the 13th to the 15th century it was common to give the same name to more than one child in a family: the second would be known, for example, as John the younger.

- *The name Jesus is highly popular in Spanish-speaking countries, but considered sacrilegious in much of northern and central Europe.*

- Changing a person's name was once a grave offence. Records in the English city of Rochester state that on Oct 15th, 1515, an Agnes Sharpe 'voluntarily changed the name of her infant son … for which she submitted penance.'

- *Many names still originate from religious history, such as Cate, Katie and Kate from Saint Catherine.*

- How a name is spelled can have religious links also. Sarah is a favourite for Christians, while Sara is preferred by Muslims.

- *The popular boy's name Aaron emerged as a variation of the Biblical Aron, thanks to Elvis Aaron Presley.*

- A name from Irish legend, Conor, has recently become popular internationally but it is often spelled Connor, which denotes a surname in Ireland!

- *Lawrence (Latin), Chloe (Greek literature) and Victoria (history) are examples of other sources for names.*

- Then there's Jack! It seems to have emerged from nowhere – but perhaps from Jankin, a version of John – to become the ubiquitous name of fairy tales and a highly-popular first name.

- *Name 'globalisation' gives us monikers like Tanya, Brooklyn and Chelsea.*

- The general decrease in formality – nobody is now known as Mr, or Mrs, Jones – leads parents to seek ever more imaginative and unique names.

- *Names popular in one country may hardly exist elsewhere. Ever heard of Seren or Cerys? Both are Top 20 names for girls in Wales.*

- Copying celebrities is popular. In 2000 Sonny Sandoval, singer with American group POD, mentioned on MTV that he had named his daughter Nevaeh ('Heaven' backwards). By 2005 more than 3,000 girls were given the name each year in the USA.

- *Finally, before opting for the latest new fab name, it would be both wise and humorous to take a listen to the Johnny Cash song 'A Boy Named Sue.'*

Christening ... Birthdays ... Christmas ...

We'll post your order to you!

Order books from this series
for postal delivery
to **anywhere in the world**.

- **Credit card bookings**:
  click the 'Purchase' link on *www.childnames.net* and follow the steps.
- **Order by post**:
  check the postage costs to your country and the accepted payment methods
  on *www.childnames.net*, then forward the total amount, with the name of
  the book(s) required and your postal address, to:

  Childnames.net, 27 Villarea Park, Glenageary, Co Dublin, Ireland.

A personalised 'My name is ...' poster for your child!

- visit *www.childnames.net*
- click on 'Posters'
- select from a range of illustrations ...
- and follow the links.

Please note:

This service is available by
mail order only (posters are
not available in bookshops).